MW00611161

Bear Takes
Brain Break

Brain Break
Kit
Dough

Empower Children with Calming Skills

Written & Illustrated by Lindsey Kealey

PAWsitive
Choices®

This book is dedicated to my husband, Thomas, who lovingly reminds me to take brain breaks while I write.

First print edition 2021

Kealey, Lindsey-author, illustrator
Bear Takes a Brain Break/Lindsey Kealey

ISBN: 978-1-7357367-6-1

Published by PAWsitive Choices, LLC
Bend, OR, USA

What is PAWsitive Choices?

PAWsitive Choices Social & Emotional Learning is an easy-to-use guide for teachers and families. It teaches social and emotional learning skills through engaging stories. Research-based strategies are interwoven throughout the curriculum to support optimal brain development and help children thrive.

PAWsitive Choices teaches you how to:

- **Solve problems**
- **Learn from mistakes**
- **Set goals**
- **Make positive choices**
- **Talk about feelings**
- **Listen and think**
- **Make healthy choices**
- **Take brain breaks**
- **Take calming breaths**
- **Use positive self-talk**

Visit www.pawsitivechoices.com to learn more.

You
Tube

PODCAST

A Note to Grown-Ups

A **brain break** is a calming practice that helps children regulate strong feelings. To integrate a brain break routine into your school or home, we suggest creating a brain break kit and finding a special place for it to be easily accessible.

Ideas for Your Brain Break Kit:

- Brain Break Steps Poster (taped to front)*
- Mirror (to identify feelings)
- Feelings Poster*
- Timer
- Play-dough
- Journal
- Paper/markers/crayons
- Breathing cards*
- Stress ball
- Book
- Stuffed animal
- Glitter Brain Frame*

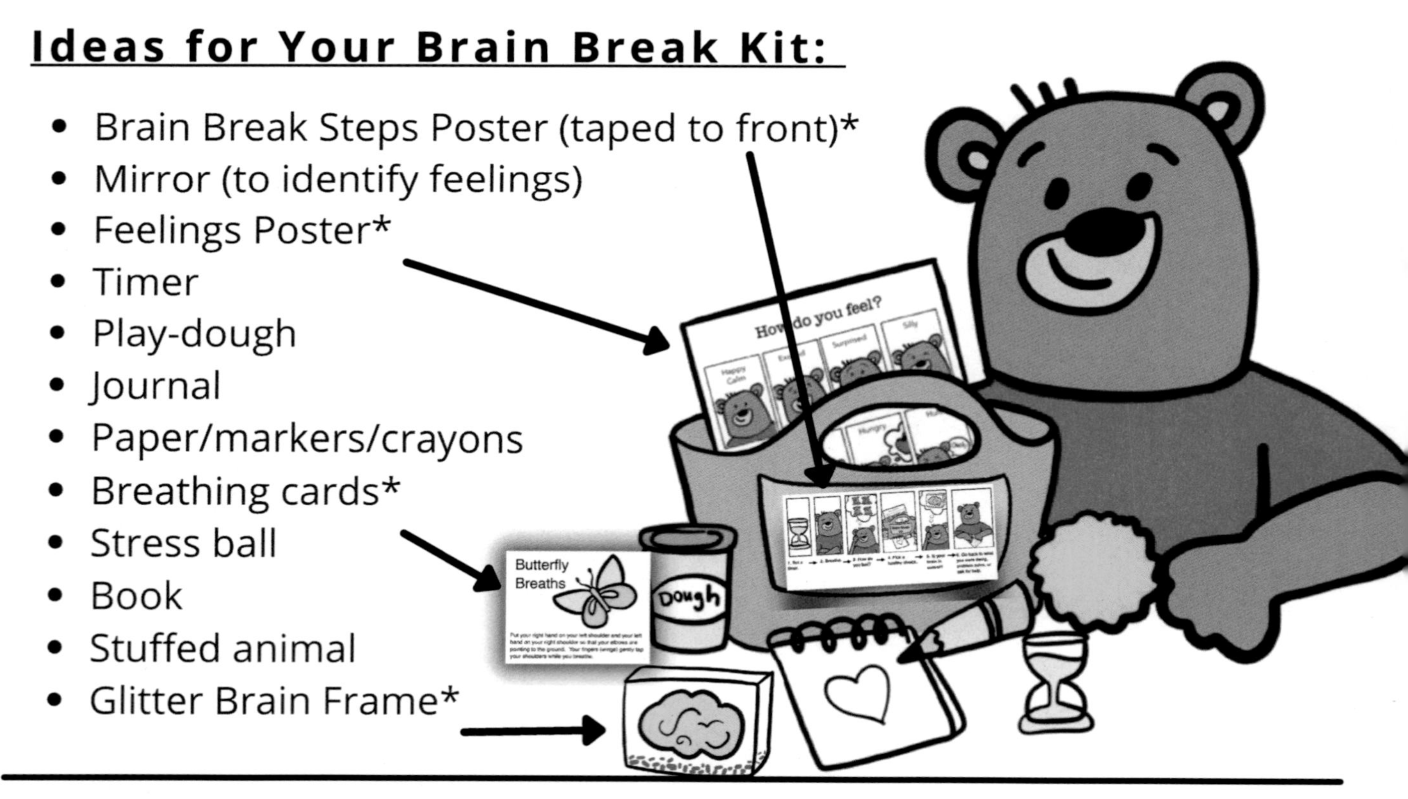
How do you feel?
Surprised
Silly
Hungry
Butterfly
Breaths
Dough

*To download and print these free posters and for other exclusive resources and videos, scan the QR code or visit: **pawsitivechoices.com/beartakesabrainbreak**. The glitter brain frame is also available for purchase here.

Table of Contents

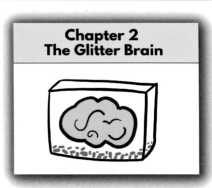

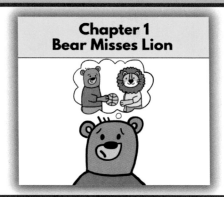

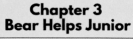

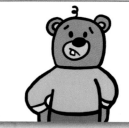

Chapter 1
Bear Misses Lion

Bear and Lion were best friends.

They read books together.

All About
the T-Rex

They played basketball together.

I'm open!

They even planned parties together.

So, when Lion was sick and couldn't go to school, Bear missed him.

Bear could hardly focus during reading time.

I miss reading with Lion.
I know what can help.

Teacher Bear showed Bear a basket called a Brain Break Kit. Inside, there were things to help him feel better.

Brain Break
Kit
Dough

Teacher Bear taught him the steps to take a brain break.

PAWsitive Choices™
Brain Break Steps
Brain Break Kit
1. Set a timer.
2. Breathe.
3. How do you feel?
4. Pick a healthy choice.
5. Is your brain in control?
6. Go ba
you were
problem solve, or
ask for help.

#1. Set a timer.*

*You can find sand timers of different lengths (e.g., 1, 5, 10, 30 minutes). Other visual timers can also be helpful.

#2. Take calming breaths.

Butterfly Breaths
Volcano Breaths

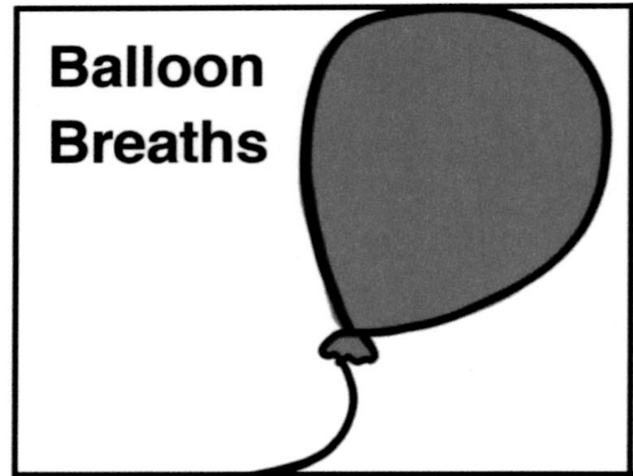
Balloon Breaths

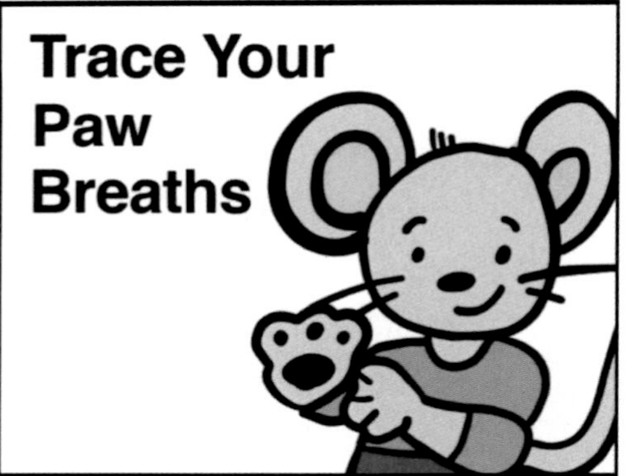
Trace Your Paw Breaths

Flower and Candle Breaths

Rub Your Ears Breaths

Scan the QR code to watch a calming breaths video.

#3. Think about how you feel.

Happy
Calm

Energetic
Silly

Disappointed
Sad

Scared
Worried
Anxious

Frustrated
Angry
Mad

Hungry
Thirsty

Feelings Tip:

You can use a feelings poster and a mirror to look at your face to help tell how you feel!

PAWsitive Choices™
How do you feel?
Happy Calm
Excited Joyful
Surprised Curious
Silly Energetic
Sleepy Tired Exhausted
Sick
Hungry Thirsty
Hurt
Ouch!
Sad Disappointed
Scared Worried Anxious
Confused
Mad Angry Frustrated
Other: _______
Chapter 7 Resource
www.pawsitivechoices.com
© 2014-2020 PAWsitive Choices, LLC.

#4. Pick a healthy choice.

Read

Make a card for someone you miss.

Draw/Color

Use play-dough or a stress ball.

Hug a stuffed animal.

Listen to music.

#5. Does your brain feel calm and in control?

#6. Finally ...

Go back to what you were doing,

problem solve, or ask for help.

Bear took three butterfly breaths and drew a picture for Lion. After taking a break, Bear felt calm and ready for reading centers!

Get well
Soon Lion!
From, Bear

Chapter 2
The Glitter Brain

The next day, Bear learned something amazing ...

He learned why taking a brain break helped him feel better.

Brain Break Kit
Dough

Teacher Bear explained, "This special picture frame has water and glitter inside. The glitter is like the chemicals in your brain. Your neurons use chemicals to send messages to each other."

The glitter shows how strong feelings can affect your thoughts.
How are thoughts and feelings different?

Feelings

Happy
Calm
Excited
Joyful
Surprised
Curious
Silly
Energetic
Sleepy
Tired
Exhausted
Sick
Hungry
Thirsty
Hurt
Ouch!
Sad
Disappointed
Scared
Worried
Anxious
Confused
Mad
Angry
Frustrated

Feelings are things you feel. You might feel sad if you miss someone.

Thoughts

Thoughts are things you think about. You might think about what you like to do with someone.

Your thoughts come from your prefrontal cortex. It is where you think and learn.

Your feelings come from a part of your brain called the limbic system.

Energetic
Silly
Disappointed
Sad
Frustrated
Angry
Mad
Scared
Worried
Anxious

When both parts work together, your brain can think, learn, and make positive choices.

When you feel calm, you can think clearly.
The glitter in this frame is not moving.
That is like your brain when you feel calm.

"Watch what happens to the glitter when it gets mixed up. This is like when you have strong feelings. It's hard to think clearly when your brain feels mixed up," said Teacher Bear.

"When you take calming breaths and think about how you feel, this helps you think clearly again. It also helps your brain feel in control of strong feelings," Teacher Bear explained.

"My brain felt mixed up yesterday. I took a brain break and that helped me feel in control of my strong feelings," shared Bear.

Brain Break Kit
Dough

"Just like Bear, anyone in the class can take a brain break when they need it. You can do a special gesture to show me you need a break," said Teacher Bear.

The Brain Break Gesture

Step 1:
Put your elbows out and your hands close to your forehead.

Step 2:
Keep your arms still and move your hands up and down.

Scan the QR to watch a tutorial video.

Teacher Bear invited Bear to teach the class how to take a brain break. Everyone loved learning from him.

Thanks Bear!
Brain Break Kit
Dough

Chapter 3
Bear Helps Junior

On the way home from school, Bear noticed that his brother, Junior, seemed sad.

How are you, Junior?

I'm sad. I can't go
to Raccoon's party.
I'm sorry, Junior.
I think I know
what can help!

When they got home, Bear grabbed his glitter brain from his backpack.

"First, take three calming breaths," said Bear.

Your brain was really upset, kind of like this mixed up brain. It's hard to think clearly when you have strong feelings.

Are strong
feelings bad?
No! They are
actually helpful
when you know
what to do
when you have
them.

"When you feel upset, you can take a break to help your brain feel in control," Bear explained.

Your Brain in Control:

When you calm your brain, your thoughts and feelings can work together. This helps your brain make positive choices, solve problems, and learn.

Your Brain NOT in Control:

It is hard for your brain to make positive choices and learn when your big feelings are stronger than your thoughts.

"Taking a brain break helps you think about your feelings so you can feel calm and in control again," said Bear.

Brain Break Kit
Dough

"Let's look around for things we can put in a brain break kit for our house," said Mom.

I want to take a brain break!

The next day before school...

Let's go to the store to get a mirror and timer for our brain break kit.
Yay!

When Bear got to school, he was excited to see Lion.

Lion's back!
Hi Bear!
Lion, I'm so glad you feel better!
SCHOOL

Thank you for your card!
I made it for you during a brain break. I'll tell you all about it!
Get well Soon Lion!
From, Bear

Comprehension Questions 

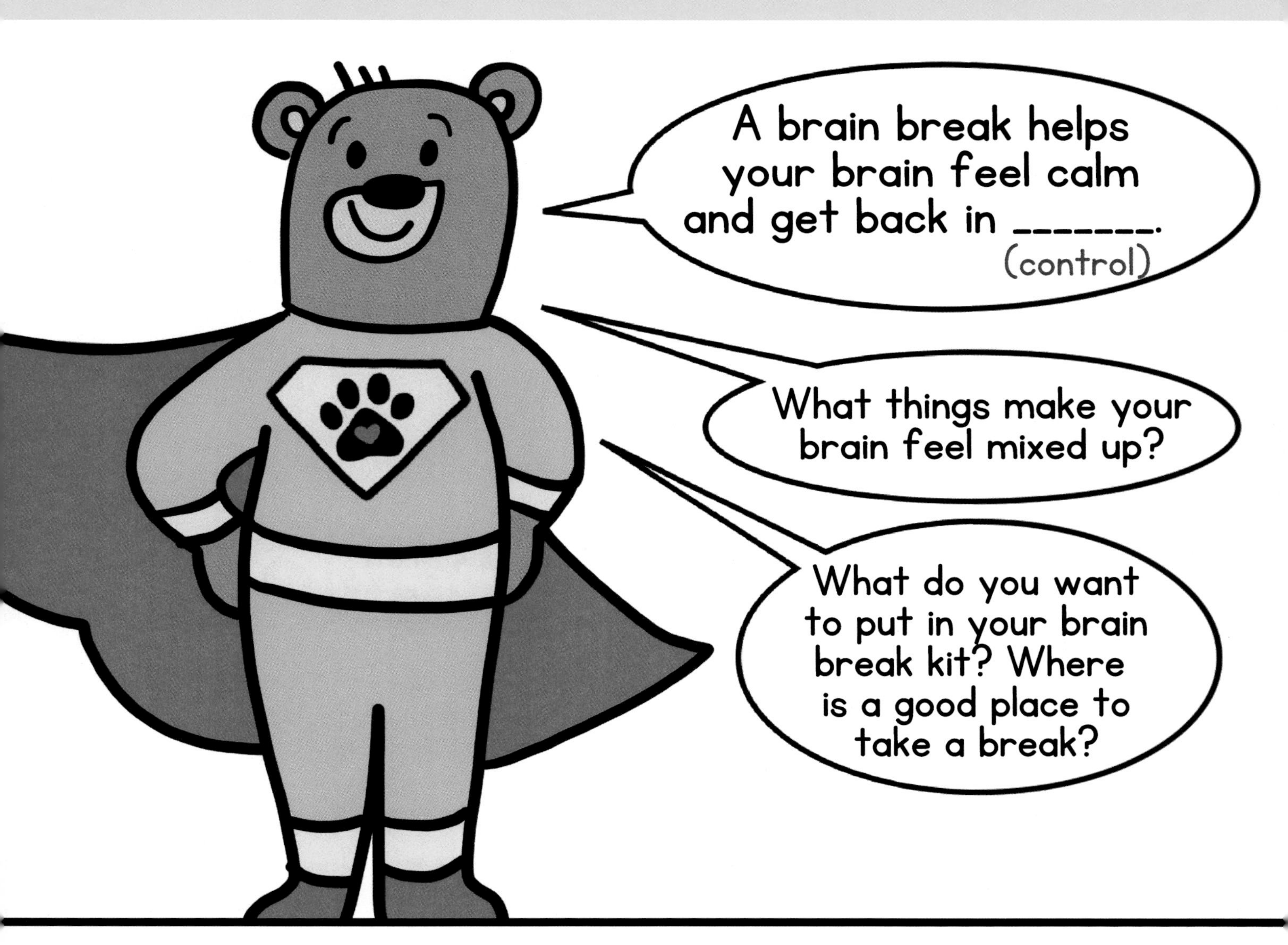
A brain break helps your brain feel calm and get back in _______.
(control)
What things make your brain feel mixed up?
What do you want to put in your brain break kit? Where is a good place to take a break?

About the Author

Lindsey Kealey is a university instructor of education, speaker, coach, and creator of PAWsitive Choices Social and Emotional Learning. She earned a Bachelor of Science in Human Development and Family Sciences with an emphasis in child development and holds a Master of Arts in Teaching. Her university work, as well as her experience teaching in public schools, helped her craft a trauma-informed curriculum that integrates neuroscience, social and emotional learning, and problem solving into a program that helps children thrive. Lindsey lives in Central Oregon and enjoys exploring the outdoors with her family and pug.

You
Tube
PODCAST

THE
PAWsitive
Choices
PODCAST
PAWsitive
Choices

For more information about PAWsitive Choices curriculum, trainings, and events, visit www.pawsitivechoices.com or send an email to info@pawsitivechoices.com. Check out The PAWsitive Choices Podcast to learn more about topics in social and emotional learning.

Check out our other books!

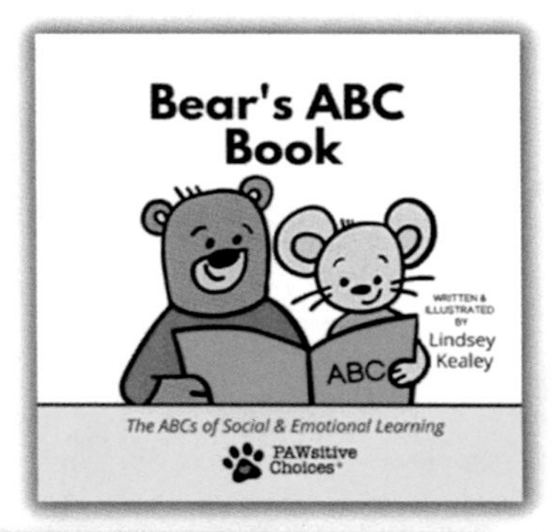
Bear's ABC Book
ABC
WRITTEN & ILLUSTRATED BY
Lindsey Kealey
The ABCs of Social & Emotional Learning
PAWsitive Choices

Bear Can Read
Sight Word Reader Book 1
Sight Words: I, can, the, we, see
WRITTEN & ILLUSTRATED BY
Lindsey Kealey
Empower Children with Social-Emotional & Literacy Skills
PAWsitive Choices

Mouse Can Read
Sight Word Reader Book 2
Sight Words: a, like, to, and, go
WRITTEN & ILLUSTRATED BY
Lindsey Kealey
Empower Children with Social-Emotional & Literacy Skills
PAWsitive Choices

Pug Solves a Problem
WRITTEN & ILLUSTRATED BY
Lindsey Kealey
Empower Children to Become Problem Solvers
PAWsitive Choices

Bear's Amazing Brain
Home Edition
A Social & Emotional Guide to Help Children Thrive
PAWsitive Choices
Written & Illustrated by Lindsey Kealey

Lion Learns to Listen
WRITTEN & ILLUSTRATED BY
Lindsey Kealey
Empower Children to Become Active Listeners
PAWsitive Choices

Pug Can Read
Sight Word Reader Book 3
Sight Words: you, do, my, are, he, help, with
WRITTEN & ILLUSTRATED BY
Lindsey Kealey
Empower Children with Social-Emotional & Literacy Skills
PAWsitive Choices

Fox Can Read
Sight Word Reader Book 4
Sight Words is, little, she was, for, have, they, of, said, want, me, here
WRITTEN & ILLUSTRATED BY
Lindsey Kealey
Empower Children with Social-Emotional & Literacy Skills
PAWsitive Choices

Lion Can Read
Sight Word Reader Book 5
Sight Words this, what, help, too, play, has, where, look, who, good, come, does
WRITTEN & ILLUSTRATED BY
Lindsey Kealey
Empower Children with Social-Emotional & Literacy Skills
PAWsitive Choices

Visit www.pawsitivechoices.com to learn more.

Made in the USA
Monee, IL
08 December 2021

83121800R00033